No Nonsense Number

Activities to support learning in Years 6 and 7

Part B

essential
resources

Suzi de Gouveia,
Jackie Andrews
and Jude Callaghan

essential
resources

Title: No Nonsense Number
Activities to support learning in Years 6 and 7 – Part B

Authors: Suzi de Gouveia, Jackie Andrews and Jude Callaghan

Editor: Tanya Tremewan

Book code: 293B

ISBN: 978-1-877523-05-2

Published: 2009

Publisher: Essential Resources Educational Publishers Limited

United Kingdom:	**Australia:**	**New Zealand:**
Unit 8–10 Parkside	PO Box 90	PO Box 5036
Shortgate Lane	Oak Flats	Invercargill
Laughton, BN8 6DG	NSW 2529	
ph: 0845 3636 147	ph: 1800 005 068	ph: 0800 087 376
fax: 0845 3636 148	fax: 1800 981 213	fax: 0800 937 825

Website: www.essentialresourcesuk.com

About the authors: Suzi is the enthusiastic headteacher of St Teresa's Primary School in Christchurch, New Zealand. She has international teaching experience and has had the pleasure of teaching in a multi-cultural environment. Over 20 years of teaching have enabled Suzi to develop a wealth of ideas and resources to best help children.

Jackie is an experienced teacher who has taught primary children in both New Zealand and the United Kingdom. As a mother of three young children she is taking time out of the classroom and is enjoying having the time to diversify.

Jude is an experienced, enthusiastic teacher with a passion for teaching and learning. Her teaching programmes are innovative and exciting. She has joined the No Nonsense Number writing team to share her deep understanding and wealth of ideas.

Contents

Introduction

This book forms part of the *No Nonsense Number* Series that supports Learning in Years 6 and 7.

Pupil templates have been included as a way reinforcing selected specific learning objectives. For each of these templates, children develop their own problems for other pupils to solve.

Answers to the problems are provided at the end of this book. Unless otherwise specified, the fractions have not been simplified. However, you may choose to encourage your pupils to do this.

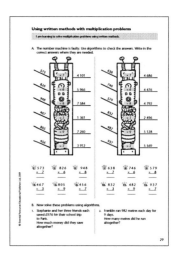

Curriculum Links

Strand	Learning objectives *Most children learn to:*
Year 6	
Counting and understanding number	• use decimal notation for tenths, hundredths and thousandths. • order a set of fractions by converting them to fractions with a common denominator. • find equivalent fractions
Calculating	• calculate mentally with integers and decimals: U.t ± U.t, TU × U, TU ÷ U. • find fractions of whole-number quantities.
Year 6 progression to Year 7	
Counting and understanding number	• order a set of fractions by converting them to decimals • knowing and using number facts • consolidate rapid recall of number facts, including multiplication facts to 10 × 10 and the associated division facts
Calculating	• understand how the commutative, associative and distributive laws, and the relationships between operations, including inverse operations, can be used to calculate more efficiently. • consolidate and extend mental methods of calculation to include fractions.

Source: Adapted from *The Primary Framework for Mathematics*, 2006.

© Essential Resources Educational Publishers Ltd 2009

Managing large numbers in multiplication problems

I am learning to manage large numbers to make multiplication easier.

Fill in the boxes to help you solve each of the equations. The first one is started for you.

1. 16 × 15 = _____

16	15	16 × 15
equals	**equals**	**equals**
_4_ × _4_	_3_ × _5_	_4_ × _4_ × _3_ × _5_ = _____

2. 35 × 18 = _____

35	18	35 × 18
equals	**equals**	**equals**
_____ × _____	_____ × _____	_____ × _____ × _____ × _____ = _____

3. 22 × 15 = _____

22	15	22 × 15
equals	**equals**	**equals**
_____ × _____	_____ × _____	_____ × _____ × _____ × _____ = _____

4. 25 × 16 = _____

25	16	25 × 16
equals	**equals**	**equals**
_____ × _____	_____ × _____	_____ × _____ × _____ × _____ = _____

5. 14 × 35 = _____

14	35	14 × 35
equals	**equals**	**equals**
_____ × _____	_____ × _____	_____ × _____ × _____ × _____ = _____

6. 45 × 24 = _____

45	24	45 × 24
equals	**equals**	**equals**
_____ × _____	_____ × _____	_____ × _____ × _____ × _____ = _____

Fill in the boxes to help you solve each of the equations.

1. 36 × 35 = _____

36	35	36 × 35
equals	equals	equals
_____ × _____	_____ × _____	_____ × _____ × _____ × _____ = _____

2. 25 × 22 = _____

25	22	25 × 22
equals	equals	equals
_____ × _____	_____ × _____	_____ × _____ × _____ × _____ = _____

3. 28 × 15 = _____

28	15	28 × 15
equals	equals	equals
_____ × _____	_____ × _____	_____ × _____ × _____ × _____ = _____

4. 35 × 16 = _____

35	16	35 × 16
equals	equals	equals
_____ × _____	_____ × _____	_____ × _____ × _____ × _____ = _____

5. 45 × 12 = _____

45	12	45 × 12
equals	equals	equals
_____ × _____	_____ × _____	_____ × _____ × _____ × _____ = _____

6. 14 × 15 = _____

14	15	14 × 15
equals	equals	equals
_____ × _____	_____ × _____	_____ × _____ × _____ × _____ = _____

I am learning to manage large numbers to make multiplication easier.

Fill in the boxes to help you solve each of the equations.

1. 22 × 15 = _____

22	15	22 × 15
equals	**equals**	**equals**
_____ × _____	_____ × _____	_____ × _____ × _____ × _____ = _____

2. 45 × 24 = _____

45	24	45 × 24
equals	**equals**	**equals**
_____ × _____	_____ × _____	_____ × _____ × _____ × _____ = _____

3. 25 × 22 = _____

25	22	25 × 22
equals	**equals**	**equals**
_____ × _____	_____ × _____	_____ × _____ × _____ × _____ = _____

4. 14 × 15 = _____

14	15	14 × 15
equals	**equals**	**equals**
_____ × _____	_____ × _____	_____ × _____ × _____ × _____ = _____

5. 16 × 25 = _____

16	25	16 × 25
equals	**equals**	**equals**
_____ × _____	_____ × _____	_____ × _____ × _____ × _____ = _____

6. 14 × 35 = _____

14	35	14 × 35
equals	**equals**	**equals**
_____ × _____	_____ × _____	_____ × _____ × _____ × _____ = _____

The headteacher needs help to complete these problems so she can write her report for an important meeting. Help her to solve each one. Show your working.

1. A class of Year 8 pupils went to watch a cricket match. There were 24 pupils in the class. The tickets cost $25 each. What was the total cost of the tickets?	**5.** The health nurse arrived at school to give 45 children a vaccination. She spent 24 minutes with each child. How many minutes did she take to complete her task?
2. Pupils in Year 6 read 16 books each during Book Week. How many books did the 25 children in the class read in total? 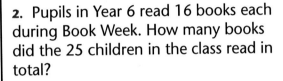	**6.** The cross country team raised funds for their trip to the national competition by running laps continually for 10 hours. There were 15 runners in the team. Each runner ran 14 laps. How many laps did they run in total in 10 hours?
3. During the Maths Challenge Competition 14 pupils each solved 35 number problems. How many problems did they solve altogether?	**7.** The 15 new entrant children each took photos of 22 objects for their alphabet books. How many photos did the teacher have to print? 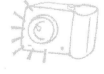
4. Year 5 pupils made slide shows of their artwork. Each of the 45 pupils made 18 slides. How many slides were made altogether? 	**8.** There were 36 families who came to Family Fun Day. Each family spent £35 during the day. How much money did they spend in total?

Using doubling and halving with multiplication problems

I am learning to solve multiplication problems using doubling and halving.

A. For each of these problems, use doubling and halving to find an easy equation. The first one is started for you.

1.
5 × 78 = _____

is the same as

<u>10</u> × <u>39</u> = _____

5.
52 × 5 = _____

is the same as

_____ × _____ = _____

9.
86 × 5 = _____

is the same as

_____ × _____ = _____

2.
46 × 5 = _____

is the same as

_____ × _____ = _____

6.
94 × 5 = _____

is the same as

_____ × _____ = _____

10.
5 × 68 = _____

is the same as

_____ × _____ = _____

3.
5 × 148 = _____

is the same as

_____ × _____ = _____

7.
462 × 5 = _____

is the same as

_____ × _____ = _____

11.
550 × 5 = _____

is the same as

_____ × _____ = _____

4.
924 × 5 = _____

is the same as

_____ × _____ = _____

8.
376 × 5 = _____

is the same as

_____ × _____ = _____

12.
5 × 572 = _____

is the same as

_____ × _____ = _____

B. Join the boxes that are the same using doubling and halving and then solve the problem. The first one is started for you.

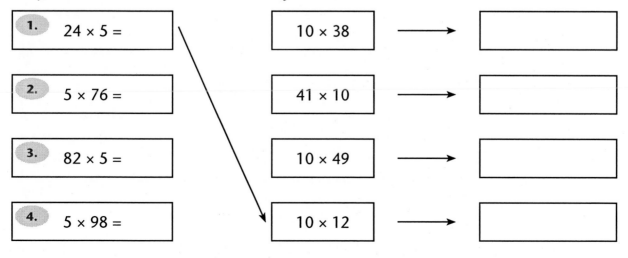

1. 24 × 5 =

2. 5 × 76 =

3. 82 × 5 =

4. 5 × 98 =

10 × 38 ⟶ [ ]

41 × 10 ⟶ [ ]

10 × 49 ⟶ [ ]

10 × 12 ⟶ [ ]

9

I am learning to solve multiplication problems using doubling and halving.

A. For each of these problems, use doubling and halving to find an easy equation. The first one is started for you.

1.
$5 \times 428 =$ _____

is the same as

__10__ $\times$ __214__ $=$ _____

5.
$284 \times 5 =$ _____

is the same as

_____ $\times$ _____ $=$ _____

9.
$516 \times 5 =$ _____

is the same as

_____ $\times$ _____ $=$ _____

2.
$172 \times 5 =$ _____

is the same as

_____ $\times$ _____ $=$ _____

6.
$650 \times 5 =$ _____

is the same as

_____ $\times$ _____ $=$ _____

10.
$5 \times 368 =$ _____

is the same as

_____ $\times$ _____ $=$ _____

3.
$5 \times 736 =$ _____

is the same as

_____ $\times$ _____ $=$ _____

7.
$902 \times 5 =$ _____

is the same as

_____ $\times$ _____ $=$ _____

11.
$844 \times 5 =$ _____

is the same as

_____ $\times$ _____ $=$ _____

4.
$628 \times 5 =$ _____

is the same as

_____ $\times$ _____ $=$ _____

8.
$946 \times 5 =$ _____

is the same as

_____ $\times$ _____ $=$ _____

12.
$5 \times 772 =$ _____

is the same as

_____ $\times$ _____ $=$ _____

B. Join the boxes that are the same using doubling and halving and then solve the problem. The first one is started for you.

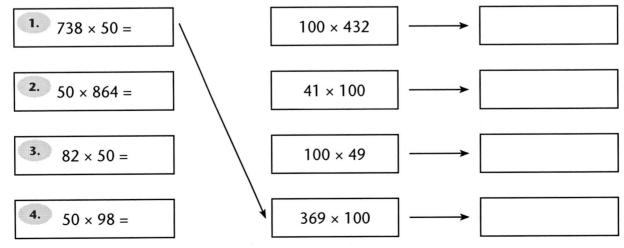

1. $738 \times 50 =$

2. $50 \times 864 =$

3. $82 \times 50 =$

4. $50 \times 98 =$

100×432

41×100

100×49

369×100

I am learning to solve multiplication problems using doubling and halving.

A. Solve these problems. Which number in each problem will you halve? Which one will you double? The first one is started for you.

1.

25 × 24 = _____

is the same as

___50___ × ___12___ = _____

___100___ × ___6___ = _____

4.

25 × 6 424 = _____

is the same as

_____ × _____ = _____

_____ × _____ = _____

2.

25 × 624 = _____

is the same as

_____ × _____ = _____

_____ × _____ = _____

5.

25 × 824 = _____

is the same as

_____ × _____ = _____

_____ × _____ = _____

3.

4 420 × 25 = _____

is the same as

_____ × _____ = _____

_____ × _____ = _____

6.

25 × 984 = _____

is the same as

_____ × _____ = _____

_____ × _____ = _____

B. Now solve this problem using the doubling and halving strategy.

The Moro Motor Racing Team is doing a stocktake. There are 684 boxes of wheel nuts, with 25 wheel nuts in each box. How many wheel nuts are there altogether?

_____ wheel nuts

A. Solve these problems. First you must decide which number to double and which one to halve for each problem.

1.

25 × 68 = _____

is the same as

_____ × _____ = _____

_____ × _____ = _____

2.

396 × 25 = _____

is the same as

_____ × _____ = _____

_____ × _____ = _____

3.

448 × 25 = _____

is the same as

_____ × _____ = _____

_____ × _____ = _____

4.

25 × 480 = _____

is the same as

_____ × _____ = _____

_____ × _____ = _____

5.

732 × 25 = _____

is the same as

_____ × _____ = _____

_____ × _____ = _____

6.

25 × 8 624 = _____

is the same as

_____ × _____ = _____

_____ × _____ = _____

B. Now solve this problem using the doubling and halving strategy.

The Moro Motor Racing Team is doing a stocktake. It counts 248 cans of fuel. Each can contains 25 litres of fuel. How many litres of fuel does the team have altogether?

_____ litres of fuel

I am learning to solve multiplication problems using doubling and halving.

A. Solve these problems using the doubling and halving strategy to find the easy equation.

1.

8 × £3.15 = _____

is the same as

_____ × _____ = _____

_____ × _____ = _____

_____ × _____ = _____

3.

12 × £4.25 = _____

is the same as

_____ × _____ = _____

_____ × _____ = _____

_____ × _____ = _____

2.

16 × £6.05 = _____

is the same as

_____ × _____ = _____

_____ × _____ = _____

_____ × _____ = _____

4.

24 × 75p= _____

is the same as

_____ × _____ = _____

_____ × _____ = _____

_____ × _____ = _____

B. Join the boxes that are the same using doubling and halving and then solve the problem. The first one is started for you.

1.
8 × £2.25 = _____

2.
12 × £1.05 = _____

3.
8 × £2.15 = _____

4.
16 × £3.25 = _____

3 × £4.20 →

2 × £8.60 →

4 × £13.00 →

2 × £9.00 →

Help Emma find the area of each of these shapes by using doubling and halving.

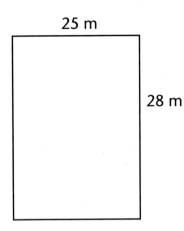

25 m

28 m

1. area = _____

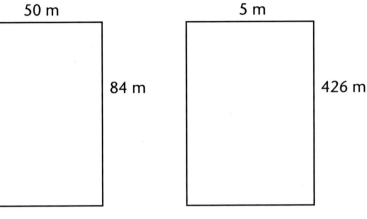

50 m

84 m

4. area = _____

5 m

426 m

7. area = _____

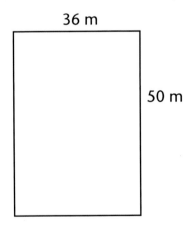

36 m

50 m

2. area = _____

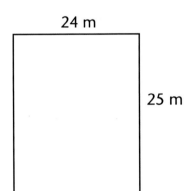

24 m

25 m

5. area = _____

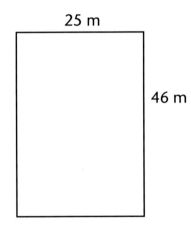

25 m

46 m

8. area = _____

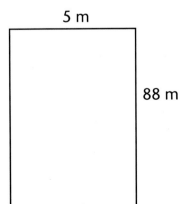

5 m

88 m

3. area = _____

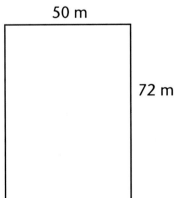

50 m

72 m

6. area = _____

5 m

24 m

9. area = _____

14

Using trebling and dividing by three with multiplication problems

I am learning to solve multiplication problems using trebling and dividing by three.

A. For each of these problems, use trebling and dividing by three to find an easy equation. The first one is started for you.

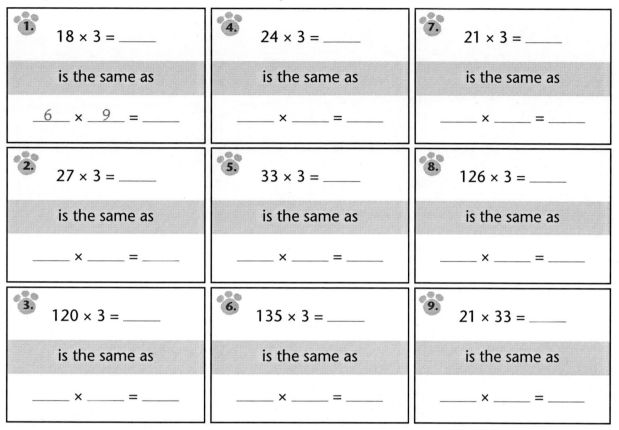

1. $18 \times 3 = \underline{\hspace{1cm}}$

is the same as

$\underline{6} \times \underline{9} = \underline{\hspace{1cm}}$

4. $24 \times 3 = \underline{\hspace{1cm}}$

is the same as

$\underline{\hspace{1cm}} \times \underline{\hspace{1cm}} = \underline{\hspace{1cm}}$

7. $21 \times 3 = \underline{\hspace{1cm}}$

is the same as

$\underline{\hspace{1cm}} \times \underline{\hspace{1cm}} = \underline{\hspace{1cm}}$

2. $27 \times 3 = \underline{\hspace{1cm}}$

is the same as

$\underline{\hspace{1cm}} \times \underline{\hspace{1cm}} = \underline{\hspace{1cm}}$

5. $33 \times 3 = \underline{\hspace{1cm}}$

is the same as

$\underline{\hspace{1cm}} \times \underline{\hspace{1cm}} = \underline{\hspace{1cm}}$

8. $126 \times 3 = \underline{\hspace{1cm}}$

is the same as

$\underline{\hspace{1cm}} \times \underline{\hspace{1cm}} = \underline{\hspace{1cm}}$

3. $120 \times 3 = \underline{\hspace{1cm}}$

is the same as

$\underline{\hspace{1cm}} \times \underline{\hspace{1cm}} = \underline{\hspace{1cm}}$

6. $135 \times 3 = \underline{\hspace{1cm}}$

is the same as

$\underline{\hspace{1cm}} \times \underline{\hspace{1cm}} = \underline{\hspace{1cm}}$

9. $21 \times 33 = \underline{\hspace{1cm}}$

is the same as

$\underline{\hspace{1cm}} \times \underline{\hspace{1cm}} = \underline{\hspace{1cm}}$

B. Join the boxes that are the same using trebling and dividing by three and then solve the problem. The first one is started for you.

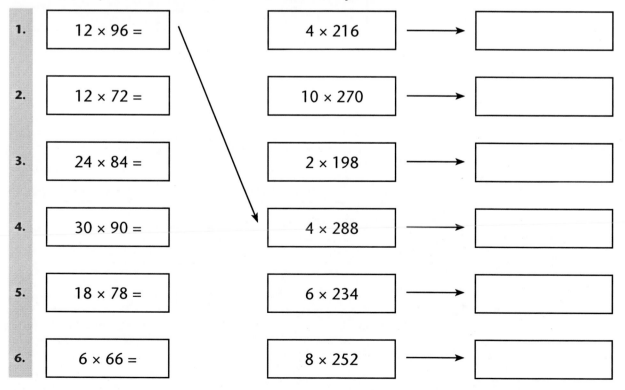

1. $12 \times 96 =$ | 4×216 $\longrightarrow$

2. $12 \times 72 =$ | 10×270 $\longrightarrow$

3. $24 \times 84 =$ | 2×198 $\longrightarrow$

4. $30 \times 90 =$ | 4×288 $\longrightarrow$

5. $18 \times 78 =$ | 6×234 $\longrightarrow$

6. $6 \times 66 =$ | 8×252 $\longrightarrow$

I am learning to solve multiplication problems using trebling and dividing by three.

A. For each of these problems, use trebling and dividing by three to find an easy equation. The first one is started for you.

1.
27 × 3 = _____

is the same as

__9__ × __9__ = _____

4.
33 × 6 = _____

is the same as

_____ × _____ = _____

7.
24 × 6 = _____

is the same as

_____ × _____ = _____

2.
39 × 6 = _____

is the same as

_____ × _____ = _____

5.
42 × 6 = _____

is the same as

_____ × _____ = _____

8.
12 × 6 = _____

is the same as

_____ × _____ = _____

3.
27 × 6 = _____

is the same as

_____ × _____ = _____

6.
36 × 6 = _____

is the same as

_____ × _____ = _____

9.
48 × 6 = _____

is the same as

_____ × _____ = _____

B. Solve the problem using trebling and dividing by three. The first one is started for you.

1. 24 × 33 =

2. 126 × 33 =

3. 27 × 33 =

4. 12 × 33 =

5. 48 × 108 =

6. 54 × 144 =

4 × 99 ⟶ [ ]

9 × 99 ⟶ [ ]

144 × 36 ⟶ [ ]

8 × 99 ⟶ [ ]

18 × 432 ⟶ [ ]

42 × 99 ⟶ [ ]

16

Using place value with multiplication and division problems

I am learning to use place value to solve multiplication problems.

A. Complete the equations. The first one is started for you.

1.

| 69 × 3 | → | _60_ × _3_ | + | _9_ × _3_ |

→ | _180_ + _____ |

→ | _____ |

2.

| 24 × 9 | → | _____ × _____ | + | _____ × _____ |

→ | _____ + _____ |

→ | _____ |

3.

| 87 × 6 | → | _____ × _____ | + | _____ × _____ |

→ | _____ + _____ |

→ | _____ |

4.

| 34 × 4 | → | _____ × _____ | + | _____ × _____ |

→ | _____ + _____ |

→ | _____ |

5.

| 19 × 8 | → | _____ × _____ | + | _____ × _____ |

→ | _____ + _____ |

→ | _____ |

B. Now solve these equations. Show your working.

1. 75 × 3 =

2. 87 × 5 =

3. 43 × 7 =

4. 38 × 4 =

5. 96 × 6 =

C. Now solve these word problems in your book. Show your working.

1. Angus bought 9 new T-shirts. Each T-shirt cost £24. How much money did Angus spend?

2. Moira and Fiona collected money from 8 friends to see "Tossing Haggis" play in town. Each person gave them £58 for the show. How much money did they collect altogether?

17

A. Complete the equations. The first one is started for you.

1. 613×7 → $\underline{600} \times \underline{7}$ + $\underline{10} \times \underline{7}$ + $\underline{3} \times \underline{7}$

→ $\underline{4\,200}$ + _____ + _____

→ _____

2. 393×9 → _____ × _____ + _____ × _____ + _____ × _____

→ _____ + _____ + _____

→ _____

3. 477×6 → _____ × _____ + _____ × _____ + _____ × _____

→ _____ + _____ + _____

→ _____

4. 802×4 → _____ × _____ + _____ × _____ + _____ × _____

→ _____ + _____ + _____

→ _____

B. Solve these equations in your book. Show your working.

1. 427×4
2. 884×5
3. 541×4
4. 139×9
5. 206×8
6. 995×6
7. 616×7
8. 568×8
9. 750×8

C. Now solve this word problem in your book. Show your working.

Hamish showed his stamp collection at school. He had 134 pages of stamps with 7 stamps on each page. How many stamps did Hamish show his friends?

I am learning to use place value to solve division problems.

A. Complete the equations. The first one is started for you.

1.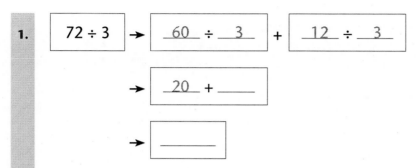
72 ÷ 3 → 60 ÷ 3 + 12 ÷ 3
→ 20 + ___
→ ___

2.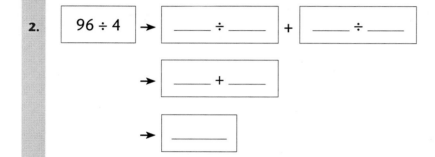
96 ÷ 4 → ___ ÷ ___ + ___ ÷ ___
→ ___ + ___
→ ___

3.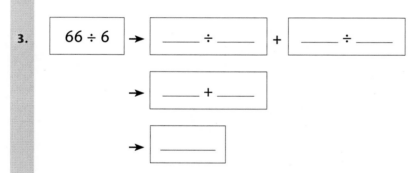
66 ÷ 6 → ___ ÷ ___ + ___ ÷ ___
→ ___ + ___
→ ___

4.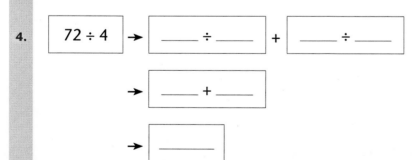
72 ÷ 4 → ___ ÷ ___ + ___ ÷ ___
→ ___ + ___
→ ___

5.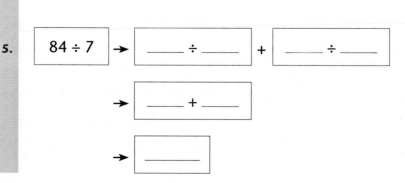
84 ÷ 7 → ___ ÷ ___ + ___ ÷ ___
→ ___ + ___
→ ___

B. Now solve these equations. Show your working.

1. 68 ÷ 4 =

2. 98 ÷ 7 =

3. 88 ÷ 8 =

4. 78 ÷ 6 =

5. 96 ÷ 6 =

C. Now solve these word problems in your book. Show your working.

1. Jemima had 96 stickers in her sticker book. They filled 3 pages with the same number of stickers on each page. How many stickers were on each page?

2. Her friend, George, had 84 stickers on 4 pages. How many stickers were on each page in George's book?

A. Complete the equations. The first one is started for you.

1. $846 \div 6$ → $\underline{600} \div \underline{6}$ + $\underline{240} \div \underline{6}$ + $\underline{6} \div \underline{6}$

→ $\underline{100}$ + _____ + _____

→ _____

2. $480 \div 4$ → ____ ÷ ____ + ____ ÷ ____ + ____ ÷ ____

→ _____ + _____ + _____

→ _____

3. $924 \div 7$ → ____ ÷ ____ + ____ ÷ ____ + ____ ÷ ____

→ _____ + _____ + _____

→ _____

4. $876 \div 6$ → ____ ÷ ____ + ____ ÷ ____ + ____ ÷ ____

→ _____ + _____ + _____

→ _____

B. Solve these equations in your book. Show your working.

1. $548 \div 4$ 4. $875 \div 7$ 7. $572 \div 4$

2. $798 \div 7$ 5. $924 \div 6$ 8. $636 \div 4$

3. $945 \div 7$ 6. $954 \div 6$ 9. $928 \div 8$

C. Now solve this word problem in your book. Show your working.

Mr Skipper has 633 magazines in his storeroom. He stored them in three equal-sized containers. How many magazines were in each container?

Using rounding and partitioning with multiplication and division problems

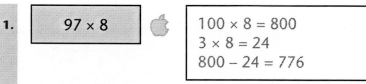

I am learning to use rounding to solve multiplication problems.

A. Solve these problems. Use the blank box to show how you do it. The first problem is solved for you.

1. 97 × 8

$$100 \times 8 = 800$$
$$3 \times 8 = 24$$
$$800 - 24 = 776$$

2. 98 × 7

3. 499 × 4

4. 69 × 9

5. 897 × 8

6. 79 × 5

7. 98 × 8

8. 399 × 9

9. 4 × 89

10. 7 × 99

B. Now solve these problems in your book. Show your working.

1. 8 × 698
2. 7 × 957
3. 4 × 899
4. 9 × 898
5. 8 × 499
6. 5 × 947
7. 8 × 798
8. 9 × 598
9. 4 × 799
10. 7 × 699
11. 6 × 698

I am learning to use partitioning to solve division problems.

A. Solve these problems. Use the blank box to show how you do it. The first problem is solved for you.

1. $627 \div 3$

$(600 \div 3) + (27 \div 3)$
$= 200 + 9$
$= 209$

2. $954 \div 6$

3. $1\ 113 \div 7$

4. $1\ 629 \div 9$

5. $1\ 248 \div 8$

6. $648 \div 4$

7. $1\ 368 \div 8$

8. $1\ 359 \div 9$

9. $1\ 176 \div 6$

10. $1\ 431 \div 9$

B. Now solve these problems in your book. Show your working.

1. $676 \div 4$

2. $1\ 253 \div 7$

3. $717 \div 3$

4. $1\ 521 \div 9$

5. $1\ 194 \div 6$

6. $1\ 272 \div 8$

7. $1\ 246 \div 7$

8. $657 \div 3$

9. $736 \div 4$

10. $1\ 183 \div 7$

Splitting numbers by factors in multiplication and division problems

I am learning to split numbers by factors to solve multiplication problems.

Complete each of the equations by showing your working on the monster's eyes and writing your answers in his mouth. The first one is done for you.

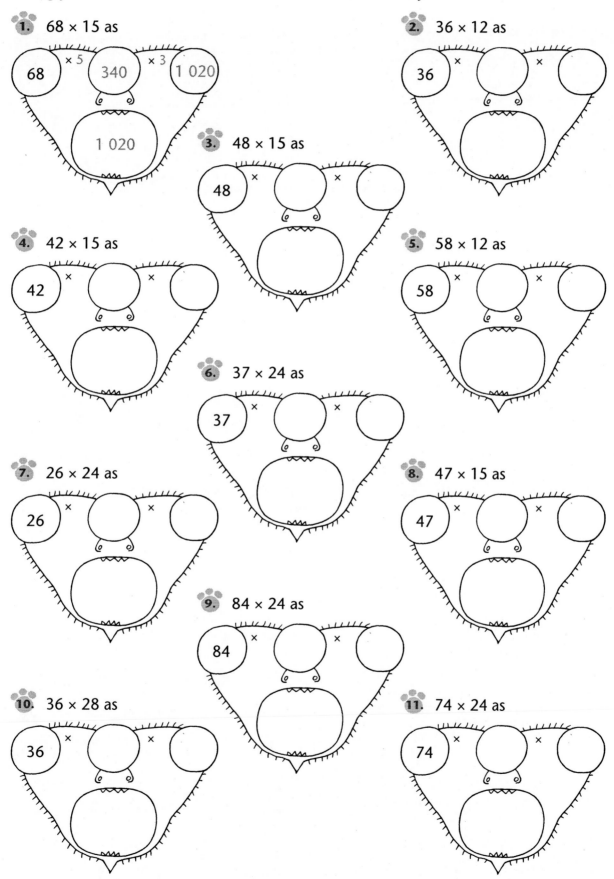

1. 68 × 15 as

68 ×5 340 ×3 1 020

1 020

2. 36 × 12 as

36 × ×

3. 48 × 15 as

48 × ×

4. 42 × 15 as

42 × ×

5. 58 × 12 as

58 × ×

6. 37 × 24 as

37 × ×

7. 26 × 24 as

26 × ×

8. 47 × 15 as

47 × ×

9. 84 × 24 as

84 × ×

10. 36 × 28 as

36 × ×

11. 74 × 24 as

74 × ×

I am learning to split numbers by factors to solve division problems.

Complete each of the equations by showing your working on the monster's eyes and writing your answer in his mouth. The first one is done for you.

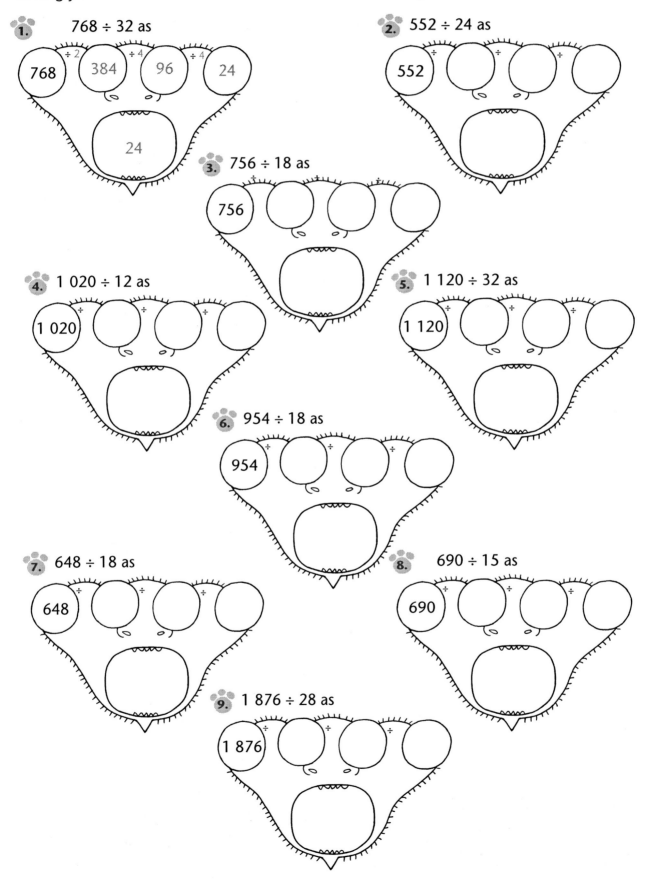

1. 768 ÷ 32 as

768 | ÷ 2 → 384 | ÷ 4 → 96 | ÷ 4 → 24

24

2. 552 ÷ 24 as

552 | ÷ | ÷ | ÷

3. 756 ÷ 18 as

756 | ÷ | ÷ | ÷

4. 1 020 ÷ 12 as

1 020 | ÷ | ÷ | ÷

5. 1 120 ÷ 32 as

1 120 | ÷ | ÷ | ÷

6. 954 ÷ 18 as

954 | ÷ | ÷ | ÷

7. 648 ÷ 18 as

648 | ÷ | ÷ | ÷

8. 690 ÷ 15 as

690 | ÷ | ÷ | ÷

9. 1 876 ÷ 28 as

1 876 | ÷ | ÷ | ÷

© Essential Resources Educational Publishers Ltd, 2009

I am learning to split numbers by factors to solve multiplication and division problems.

A. Split one of the numbers by factors to make it easier to solve each of these multiplication problems. Fill in only the carriages that you need. The first one is done for you.

1. 18×26 | 26×2 → 52×3 → 156×3 | $=$ | 468

2. 23×48

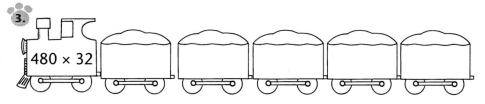

3. 480×32

4. 56×18

5. 48×54

6. 23×45

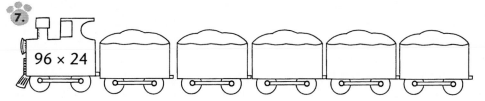

7. 96×24

8. 24×51

B. Solve these problems in your book in the same way. Show your working.

1. $896 \div 32 =$

2. $54 \times 23 =$

3. $1\ 404 \div 18 =$

4. $43 \times 45 =$

5. $78 \times 24 =$

6. $483 \div 21 =$

7. $1\ 224 \div 24 =$

8. $37 \times 48 =$

9. $1\ 035 \div 45 =$

10. $32 \times 67 =$

I am learning to split numbers by factors to solve multiplication and division problems.

Split one of the numbers by factors to make it easier to solve each of these multiplication problems. Fill in only the carriages that you need.

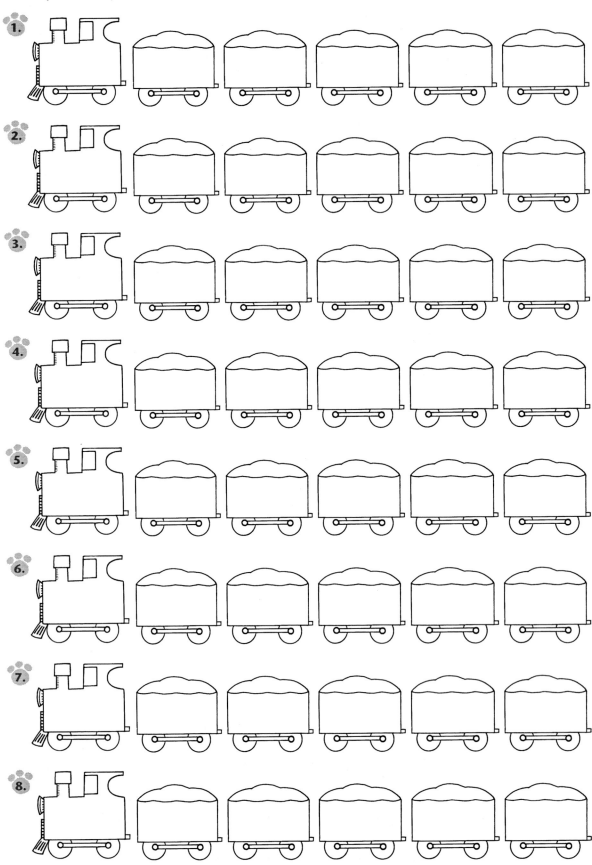

1.

2.

3.

4.

5.

6.

7.

8.

Exploring strategies to solve division problems

I am learning to solve division problems by changing them to problems that have the same answer.

Complete the equations. The first one is done for you.

1.	$140 \div 28$	→	$70 \div 14$	→	$35 \div 7$	→	5
2.	$84 \div 28$	→		→		→	
3.	$224 \div 32$	→		→		→	
4.	$168 \div 24$	→		→		→	
5.	$288 \div 36$	→		→		→	
6.	$272 \div 8$	→		→		→	
7.	$144 \div 16$	→		→		→	
8.	$216 \div 36$	→		→		→	
9.	$390 \div 15$	→		→		→	
10.	$180 \div 36$	→		→		→	
11.	$624 \div 24$	→		→		→	
12.	$384 \div 24$	→		→		→	
13.	$252 \div 36$	→		→		→	
14.	$248 \div 8$	→		→		→	
15.	$192 \div 32$	→		→		→	
16.	$324 \div 36$	→		→		→	

I am learning to solve division problems using place value, including written methods.

A. Complete the equations. The first one is done for you.

1. $3\overline{)2\,5\,5}$ (85)	**7.** $5\overline{)3\,4\,5}$	**13.** $6\overline{)4\,4\,4}$	**19.** $4\overline{)3\,2\,4}$	**25.** $3\overline{)1\,5\,6}$
2. $7\overline{)2\,8\,7}$	**8.** $6\overline{)5\,6\,4}$	**14.** $4\overline{)6\,5\,6}$	**20.** $9\overline{)5\,4\,9}$	**26.** $8\overline{)6\,6\,4}$
3. $3\overline{)1\,0\,5}$	**9.** $7\overline{)3\,7\,1}$	**15.** $9\overline{)2\,4\,3}$	**21.** $5\overline{)2\,4\,0}$	**27.** $3\overline{)2\,2\,8}$
4. $9\overline{)7\,7\,4}$	**10.** $4\overline{)1\,4\,4}$	**16.** $6\overline{)3\,2\,4}$	**22.** $5\overline{)2\,1\,0}$	**28.** $5\overline{)4\,3\,5}$
5. $4\overline{)2\,5\,2}$	**11.** $8\overline{)6\,1\,6}$	**17.** $9\overline{)7\,9\,2}$	**23.** $4\overline{)1\,5\,6}$	**29.** $6\overline{)1\,6\,8}$
6. $7\overline{)6\,2\,3}$	**12.** $3\overline{)1\,9\,2}$	**18.** $8\overline{)6\,2\,4}$	**24.** $9\overline{)3\,8\,7}$	**30.** $4\overline{)2\,2\,4}$

B. Solve these problems.

1. Thomas and his four friends were fundraising to pay for their trip to London to compete in a National Under 11s Cricket Competition. They raised £170 doing a sponsored run.
How much money did each of them get to go towards the cost of their trip?

3. Jeanne went to the public library and got out 9 talking books. They had a total of 315 minutes playing time and they all played for the same length of time.
How many minutes did each book play for?

2. Eight of the Year 6 children from St Teresa's Primary packed 496 bags of popcorn for the school gala. How many bags did each pupil pack?

4. Gabi and her 5 friends entered a coin balancing competition. Together they balanced 330 coins. If they all balanced the same number how many would Gabi have balanced?

Using written methods with multiplication problems

I am learning to solve multiplication problems using written methods.

A. The number machine is faulty. Use algorithms to check the answers. Write in the correct answers where they are needed.

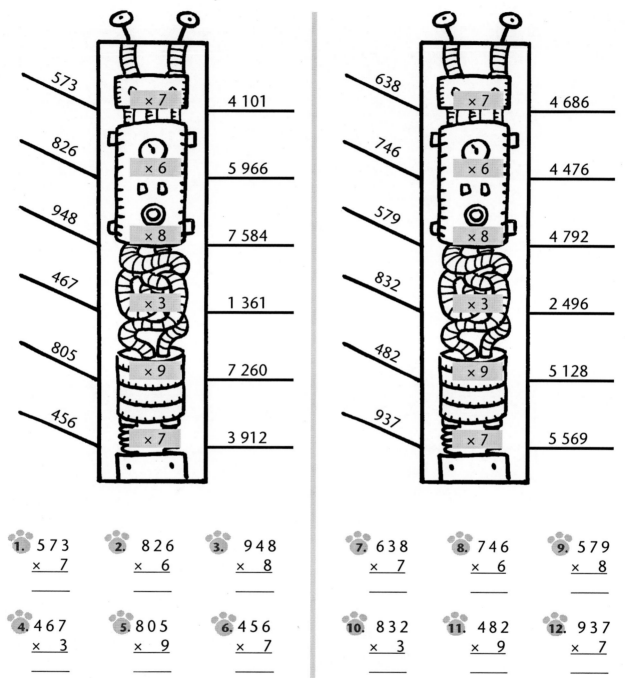

1. 573	**2.** 826	**3.** 948	**7.** 638	**8.** 746	**9.** 579
× 7	× 6	× 8	× 7	× 6	× 8
———	———	———	———	———	———
4. 467	**5.** 805	**6.** 456	**10.** 832	**11.** 482	**12.** 937
× 3	× 9	× 7	× 3	× 9	× 7
———	———	———	———	———	———

B. Now solve these problems using algorithms.

1. Stephanie and her three friends each saved £976 for their school trip to Paris.
   How much money did they save altogether?

2. Franklin ran 982 metres each day for 9 days.
   How many metres did he run altogether?

29

Choosing the best problem-solving strategy

I am learning to choose the best strategy to solve a problem.

Circle the strategy you would choose to solve the problem. Justify your choice and then solve the problem.

	Problem	Strategy	Justification	Answer
1.	5 × 428	Place value Compensation Doubling and halving Changing the problem		
2.	897 × 8	Place value Compensation Doubling and halving Changing the problem		
3.	24 × 33	Place value Compensation Doubling and halving Changing the problem		
4.	24 × 25	Place value Compensation Doubling and halving Changing the problem		
5.	287 × 6	Place value Compensation Doubling and halving Changing the problem		
6.	96 ÷ 6	Place value Compensation Doubling and halving Changing the problem		
7.	192 ÷ 32	Place value Compensation Doubling and halving Changing the problem		

Circle the strategy you would choose to solve the problem. Justify your choice and then solve the problem.

	Problem	Strategy	Justification	Answer
1.	738 × 50	Place value Compensation Doubling and halving Changing the problem		
2.	4 × 89	Place value Compensation Doubling and halving Changing the problem		
3.	12 × 33	Place value Compensation Doubling and halving Changing the problem		
4.	25 × 46	Place value Compensation Doubling and halving Changing the problem		
5.	138 × 4	Place value Compensation Doubling and halving Changing the problem		
6.	484 ÷ 4	Place value Compensation Doubling and halving Changing the problem		
7.	216 ÷ 36	Place value Compensation Doubling and halving Changing the problem		

Converting a fraction to equivalent fractions

I am learning to convert a fraction to any equivalent fraction.

A. Complete these number machines. The first one is started for you.

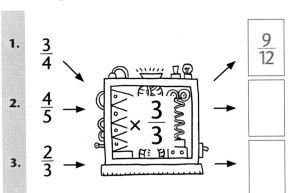

1. $\dfrac{3}{4}$ $\dfrac{9}{12}$

2. $\dfrac{4}{5}$

3. $\dfrac{2}{3}$

7. $\dfrac{4}{5}$

8. $\dfrac{1}{3}$

9. $\dfrac{6}{10}$

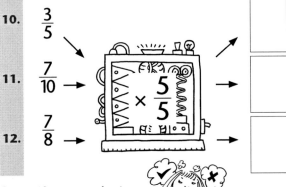

4. $\dfrac{5}{8}$

5. $\dfrac{1}{5}$

6. $\dfrac{2}{3}$

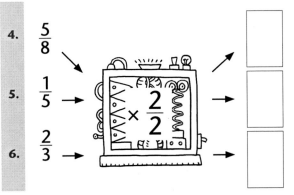

10. $\dfrac{3}{5}$

11. $\dfrac{7}{10}$

12. $\dfrac{7}{8}$

B. Are the following statements true or false? Justify your choice.

1. $\dfrac{3}{4} = \dfrac{18}{24}$ | **True** / **False** | Justify:

2. $\dfrac{5}{6} = \dfrac{40}{54}$ | **True** / **False** | Justify:

3. $\dfrac{3}{8} = \dfrac{30}{72}$ | **True** / **False** | Justify:

4. $\dfrac{32}{48} = \dfrac{3}{4}$ | **True** / **False** | Justify:

5. $\dfrac{56}{64} = \dfrac{7}{8}$ | **True** / **False** | Justify:

I am learning to convert a fraction to any equivalent fraction.

Circle the two fractions that are equivalent. Show your working.

1.	$\frac{3}{4}$ $\frac{4}{5}$ $\frac{15}{20}$	
2.	$\frac{30}{40}$ $\frac{28}{32}$ $\frac{7}{8}$	
3.	$\frac{16}{24}$ $\frac{20}{30}$ $\frac{15}{20}$	
4.	$\frac{1}{4}$ $\frac{5}{12}$ $\frac{25}{60}$	
5.	$\frac{6}{15}$ $\frac{12}{36}$ $\frac{4}{12}$	
6.	$\frac{2}{7}$ $\frac{16}{24}$ $\frac{16}{56}$	
7.	$\frac{20}{25}$ $\frac{6}{10}$ $\frac{45}{75}$	
8.	$\frac{16}{30}$ $\frac{16}{40}$ $\frac{14}{35}$	
9.	$\frac{20}{32}$ $\frac{35}{42}$ $\frac{40}{64}$	
10.	$\frac{21}{32}$ $\frac{18}{24}$ $\frac{6}{8}$	

Adding and subtracting fractions with different denominators

I am learning to add fractions with different denominators.

A. Solve these problems. Use the blank box to show how you do it. The first problem is started for you.

1. $\dfrac{3}{5} + \dfrac{1}{4}$

$$\frac{3}{5} \times \frac{4}{4} = \frac{12}{20} \qquad \frac{1}{4} \times \frac{5}{5} = \frac{5}{20} \qquad\qquad \frac{12}{20} + \frac{5}{20} =$$

2. $\dfrac{2}{6} + \dfrac{3}{8}$

3. $\dfrac{3}{4} + \dfrac{11}{12}$

4. $\dfrac{4}{5} + \dfrac{2}{3}$

5. $\dfrac{2}{3} + \dfrac{6}{8}$

6. $\dfrac{4}{9} + \dfrac{3}{6}$

B. What numbers does the sun make? Show your working in the space provided.

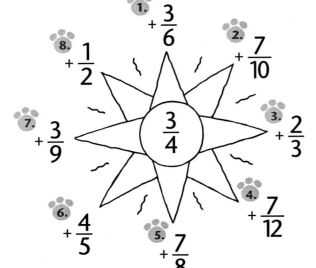

I am learning to add fractions with different denominators.

A. Solve these problems. Use the blank box to show how you do it.

1. $\dfrac{3}{4} + \dfrac{1}{8}$

2. $\dfrac{4}{6} + \dfrac{3}{4}$

3. $\dfrac{3}{5} + \dfrac{2}{4}$

4. $\dfrac{4}{8} + \dfrac{3}{4}$

5. $\dfrac{2}{3} + \dfrac{9}{12}$

6. $\dfrac{1}{2} + \dfrac{5}{8}$

B. Use your knowledge of adding fractions to work out the fractions that come out of the number machines. Simplify the answers.

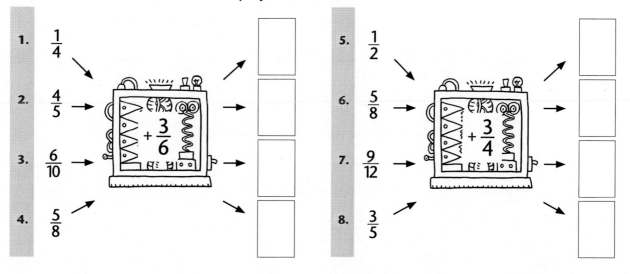

1. $\dfrac{1}{4}$

2. $\dfrac{4}{5}$

3. $\dfrac{6}{10}$

4. $\dfrac{5}{8}$

$+\dfrac{3}{6}$

5. $\dfrac{1}{2}$

6. $\dfrac{5}{8}$

7. $\dfrac{9}{12}$

8. $\dfrac{3}{5}$

$+\dfrac{3}{4}$

I am learning to subtract fractions with different denominators.

A. Link the boxes in the left-hand and middle columns to help you solve each equation.

1. $\dfrac{4}{5} - \dfrac{1}{2}$

a. $\dfrac{16}{20} - \dfrac{15}{20}$

2. $\dfrac{6}{10} - \dfrac{2}{5}$

b. $\dfrac{8}{10} - \dfrac{5}{10}$

3. $\dfrac{3}{4} - \dfrac{3}{5}$

c. $\dfrac{12}{15} - \dfrac{10}{15}$

4. $\dfrac{4}{5} - \dfrac{2}{3}$

d. $\dfrac{6}{10} - \dfrac{4}{10}$

5. $\dfrac{8}{10} - \dfrac{3}{4}$

e. $\dfrac{15}{20} - \dfrac{12}{20}$

B. Solve these problems. Use the blank box to show how you do it.

1. $\dfrac{6}{12} - \dfrac{1}{3}$

2. $\dfrac{7}{8} - \dfrac{1}{2}$

3. $\dfrac{14}{20} - \dfrac{1}{5}$

4. $\dfrac{5}{6} - \dfrac{2}{3}$

A. Link the boxes in the left-hand and middle columns to help you solve each equation.

1. $\frac{3}{5} - \frac{1}{3}$

a. $\frac{14}{18} - \frac{9}{18}$

2. $\frac{7}{9} - \frac{3}{6}$

b. $\frac{16}{24} - \frac{9}{24}$

3. $\frac{5}{6} - \frac{3}{4}$

c. $\frac{9}{15} - \frac{5}{15}$

4. $\frac{2}{3} - \frac{3}{8}$

d. $\frac{2}{3} - \frac{2}{3}$

5. $\frac{10}{15} - \frac{4}{6}$

e. $\frac{10}{12} - \frac{9}{12}$

B. Solve these problems. Use the blank box to show how you do it.

1. $\frac{6}{9} - \frac{1}{2}$

2. $\frac{7}{8} - \frac{2}{3}$

3. $\frac{7}{8} - \frac{4}{5}$

4. $\frac{3}{4} - \frac{3}{5}$

37

Finding fractions

I am learning how to find fractions of amounts.

A. Solve the following problems. The first one is done for you.

1. $\frac{3}{4} \times 8 = \frac{24}{4} = 6$

2. $\frac{7}{8} \times 9 = \underline{\hspace{1cm}} = \underline{\hspace{1cm}}$

3. $\frac{7}{10} \times 9 = \underline{\hspace{1cm}} = \underline{\hspace{1cm}}$

4. $\frac{2}{5} \times 9 = \underline{\hspace{1cm}} = \underline{\hspace{1cm}}$

5. $\frac{2}{3} \times 9 = \underline{\hspace{1cm}} = \underline{\hspace{1cm}}$

6. $\frac{4}{9} \times 9 = \underline{\hspace{1cm}} = \underline{\hspace{1cm}}$

7. $\frac{7}{8} \times 4 = \underline{\hspace{1cm}} = \underline{\hspace{1cm}}$

8. $\frac{2}{6} \times 9 = \underline{\hspace{1cm}} = \underline{\hspace{1cm}}$

9. $\frac{3}{5} \times 9 = \underline{\hspace{1cm}} = \underline{\hspace{1cm}}$

B. Link the columns to help you solve each equation.
The first one is started for you.

1.	$\frac{3}{4} \times 4$	$\frac{36}{8}$	$7\frac{7}{8}$
2.	$\frac{7}{8} \times 9$	$\frac{12}{4}$	$6\frac{2}{3}$
3.	$\frac{5}{6} \times 8$	$\frac{18}{3}$	3
4.	$\frac{3}{8} \times 12$	$\frac{63}{8}$	$4\frac{1}{2}$
5.	$\frac{2}{3} \times 9$	$\frac{40}{6}$	6

C. Fill in the missing numbers.

1. $\frac{3}{4} \times \underline{\hspace{0.5cm}} = \frac{}{4} = 3\frac{3}{4}$

2. $\frac{2}{3} \times \underline{\hspace{0.5cm}} = \frac{}{3} = 2\frac{2}{3}$

3. $\frac{5}{8} \times \underline{\hspace{0.5cm}} = \frac{}{8} = 5\frac{5}{8}$

4. $\frac{3}{8} \times \underline{\hspace{0.5cm}} = \frac{}{8} = 1\frac{4}{8}$

5. $\frac{3}{8} \times \underline{\hspace{0.5cm}} = \frac{}{8} = 1\frac{1}{8}$

6. $\frac{5}{6} \times \underline{\hspace{0.5cm}} = \frac{}{6} = 4\frac{1}{6}$

7. $\frac{3}{4} \times \underline{\hspace{0.5cm}} = \frac{}{4} = 5\frac{1}{4}$

8. $\frac{5}{8} \times \underline{\hspace{0.5cm}} = \frac{}{8} = 1\frac{7}{8}$

9. $\frac{2}{3} \times \underline{\hspace{0.5cm}} = \frac{}{3} = 4$

10. $\frac{2}{3} \times \underline{\hspace{0.5cm}} = \frac{}{3} = 4\frac{2}{3}$

11. $\frac{2}{5} \times \underline{\hspace{0.5cm}} = \frac{}{5} = 2\frac{4}{5}$

Ordering fractions without calculations

I am learning to order fractions without calculations.

Are the following statements true or false? Justify your choice.

1. $1 - \frac{17}{36} > \frac{1}{2}$

True
False

Justify:

2. $\frac{24}{42} + \frac{6}{12} < 1$

True
False

Justify:

3. $\frac{6}{10} - \frac{12}{60} \leqslant \frac{1}{2}$

True
False

Justify:

4. $\frac{12}{48} + \frac{40}{100} \geqslant \frac{1}{2}$

True
False

Justify:

5. $\frac{5}{12} + \frac{18}{30} < 1$

True
False

Justify:

6. $1 - \frac{18}{30} > \frac{1}{2}$

True
False

Justify:

7. $\frac{12}{16} + \frac{30}{100} > 1$

True
False

Justify:

8. $1 - \frac{20}{30} < \frac{1}{2}$

True
False

Justify:

I am learning to order fractions without calculations.

Write some fraction statements in the spaces on the left. Make some of them true and some of them false. Give your equations to a partner to solve.

Are the following statements true or false? Justify your choice.

1. | **True** **False** | Justify: |

2. | **True** **False** | Justify: |

3. | **True** **False** | Justify: |

4. | **True** **False** | Justify: |

5. | **True** **False** | Justify: |

6. | **True** **False** | Justify: |

7. | **True** **False** | Justify: |

8. | **True** **False** | Justify: |

Introducing mixed numbers and common fractions

I am learning about mixed numbers and common fractions.

Write out each statement again, filling in the missing number.

1. $2\frac{1}{4} < \frac{\square}{4} < 2\frac{3}{4}$ _____

2. $\frac{10}{2} < \square\frac{1}{2} < \frac{12}{2}$ _____

3. $3\frac{2}{5} < \frac{\square}{5} < 3\frac{4}{5}$ _____

4. $\frac{14}{4} < 3\frac{\square}{4} < \frac{16}{4}$ _____

5. $\frac{17}{5} < \square\frac{3}{5} < \frac{19}{5}$ _____

6. $2\frac{3}{10} < \frac{\square}{10} < 2\frac{5}{10}$ _____

7. $\frac{17}{4} < \square\frac{2}{4} < \frac{19}{4}$ _____

8. $\frac{11}{5} < 2\frac{\square}{5} < \frac{13}{5}$ _____

9. $\frac{7}{3} < 2\frac{\square}{3} < \frac{9}{3}$ _____

10. $\frac{13}{6} < \square\frac{2}{6} < \frac{15}{6}$ _____

11. $2\frac{3}{8} < \frac{\square}{8} < 2\frac{5}{8}$ _____

12. $3\frac{3}{4} < \frac{\square}{4} < 4\frac{1}{4}$ _____

13. $\frac{13}{6} < \square\frac{1}{3} < \frac{15}{6}$ _____

14. $\frac{20}{9} < 2\frac{\square}{9} < \frac{22}{9}$ _____

15. $3\frac{3}{5} < \frac{\square}{5} < 4$ _____

16. $\frac{21}{9} < \square\frac{\square}{9} < \frac{23}{9}$ _____

Help each child feed their own dog by drawing a line from the mixed number in the dog's coat to its equivalent common fraction on the can.

Multiplying fractions

I am learning to multiply fractions.

Use the boxes to help you find the answers. The first one is done for you.

1. $\frac{3}{4} \times \frac{1}{3} =$

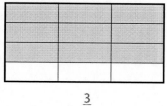   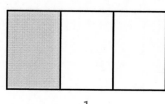   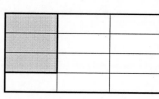

_____ $\frac{3}{4}$ _____   ×   _____ $\frac{1}{3}$ _____   so $\frac{3}{4}$ of $\frac{1}{3} = \frac{3}{12}$ so $\frac{3}{4} \times \frac{1}{3} = \frac{3}{12}$

2. $\frac{1}{2} \times \frac{3}{8} =$

   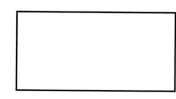   

_____   ×   _____   so   _____

3. $\frac{4}{5} \times \frac{1}{2} =$

   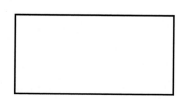   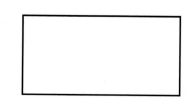

_____   ×   _____   so   _____

4. $\frac{2}{3} \times \frac{1}{4} =$

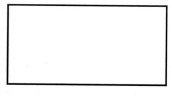   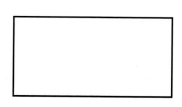   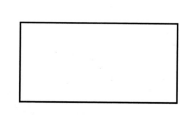

_____   ×   _____   so   _____

5. $\frac{3}{4} \times \frac{1}{4} =$

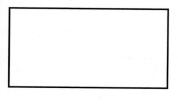

_____   ×   _____   so   _____

43

Use the boxes to help you find the answers.

1. $\frac{1}{2} \times \frac{2}{3} =$

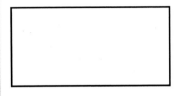 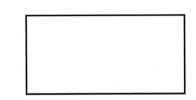 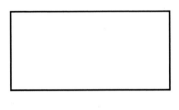

_____ × _____ so _____

2. $\frac{3}{4} \times \frac{2}{3} =$

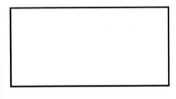 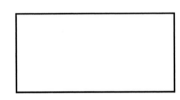 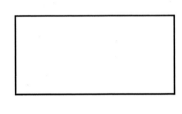

_____ × _____ so _____

3. $\frac{3}{4} \times \frac{3}{5} =$

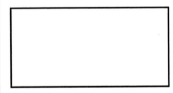  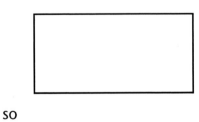

_____ × _____ so _____

4. $\frac{2}{3} \times \frac{2}{5} =$

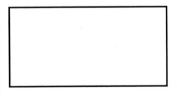 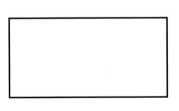 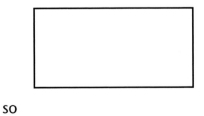

_____ × _____ so _____

5. $\frac{7}{8} \times \frac{1}{2} =$

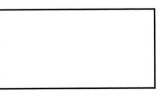 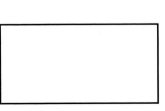 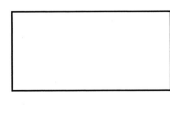

_____ × _____ so _____

44

A. Match the equations to their answers.

1. $\frac{3}{4} \times \frac{5}{6}$	**a.** $\frac{14}{24}$	**6.** $\frac{21}{32}$	**f.** $\frac{2}{3} \times \frac{2}{3}$
2. $\frac{7}{8} \times \frac{2}{3}$	**b.** $\frac{21}{72}$	**7.** $\frac{15}{40}$	**g.** $\frac{7}{8} \times \frac{3}{4}$
3. $\frac{5}{6} \times \frac{2}{4}$	**c.** $\frac{15}{24}$	**8.** $\frac{18}{30}$	**h.** $\frac{9}{10} \times \frac{2}{3}$
4. $\frac{3}{8} \times \frac{7}{9}$	**d.** $\frac{12}{20}$	**9.** $\frac{4}{9}$	**i.** $\frac{5}{6} \times \frac{8}{9}$
5. $\frac{4}{5} \times \frac{3}{4}$	**e.** $\frac{10}{24}$	**10.** $\frac{40}{54}$	**j.** $\frac{3}{5} \times \frac{5}{8}$

B. Help the number machines process the numbers.

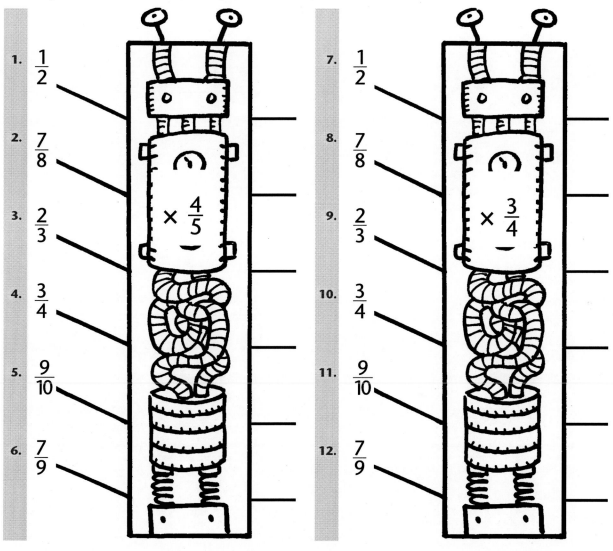

1. $\frac{1}{2}$ **7.** $\frac{1}{2}$

2. $\frac{7}{8}$ **8.** $\frac{7}{8}$

3. $\frac{2}{3}$ **9.** $\frac{2}{3}$

4. $\frac{3}{4}$ **10.** $\frac{3}{4}$

5. $\frac{9}{10}$ **11.** $\frac{9}{10}$

6. $\frac{7}{9}$ **12.** $\frac{7}{9}$

(left machine: $\times \frac{4}{5}$; right machine: $\times \frac{3}{4}$)

Finding fractions between two other fractions

Mark and Karen are responsible for feeding the animals at Whattle Zoo. Doctor Domuch's book, *The Dummies' Guide to Zoo Keeping*, tells them that the animals must only eat a part of a bale of hay but that amount differs for each kind of animal. Help them work out how much they must feed each animal.

In each box, make the two fractions into **equivalent fractions** with a common denominator then name a fraction between them.

1. Springbok eats between $\frac{2}{5}$ and $\frac{3}{4}$ of a bale.

2. Mammoth eats between $\frac{2}{3}$ and $\frac{7}{8}$ of a bale.

3. Giraffe eats between $\frac{7}{10}$ and $\frac{3}{4}$ of a bale.

4. Elephant eats between $\frac{13}{25}$ and $\frac{1}{2}$ of a bale.

5. Rhino eats between $\frac{3}{8}$ and $\frac{2}{5}$ of a bale.

6. Yak eats between $\frac{6}{8}$ and $\frac{17}{25}$ of a bale.

7. Highland Cow eats between $\frac{4}{6}$ and $\frac{23}{25}$ of a bale.

Mark and Karen are responsible for feeding the animals at Whattle Zoo. Doctor Domuch's book, *The Dummies' Guide to Zoo Keeping*, tells them that the animals must only eat a part of a bale of hay but that amount differs for each kind of animal. Help them work out how much they must feed each animal.

In each box, provided make the two fractions into **decimal fractions** and then name a decimal fraction between them.

1. Springbok eats between
   $\frac{2}{5}$ and $\frac{3}{4}$ of a bale.

2. Mammoth eats between
   $\frac{2}{3}$ and $\frac{7}{8}$ of a bale.

3. Giraffe eats between
   $\frac{7}{10}$ and $\frac{3}{4}$ of a bale.

4. Elephant eats between
   $\frac{13}{25}$ and $\frac{1}{2}$ of a bale.

5. Rhino eats between
   $\frac{3}{8}$ and $\frac{2}{5}$ of a bale.

6. Yak eats between
   $\frac{6}{8}$ and $\frac{17}{25}$ of a bale.

7. Highland Cow eats between
   $\frac{4}{6}$ and $\frac{23}{25}$ of a bale.

Solving fractions of whole numbers

I am learning to find fractions of whole numbers.

Solve these problems. The first one is done for you.

1. Amy had a box of 12 chocolates. She shared a third of the box with her friend. She then shared three quarters of what was left with her sisters. How many did she have left?

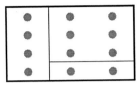 → $\frac{1}{3}$ of 12 = 4 $\frac{3}{4}$ of 8 = 6   She had 2 left.

2. Joseph had a box of 12 apples. He shared one half of the box with his friend. He then shared one third of what was left with his sisters. How many did he have left?

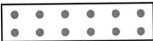 →

3. Caitlin had a bag of 24 snake sweets. She shared three quarters of the bag with Gracie. She then shared five sixths of what was left with her brother Nicholas. How many did she have left?

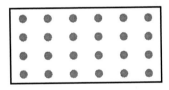 →

4. Gabi had a box of 24 chocolates. She shared five eighths of the box with her friend. She then shared two thirds of what was left with her sisters. How many did she share with her sisters?

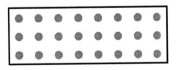 →

5. Thomas had a box of 24 lollipops. He shared five twelfths of the box with his friend. He then shared half of what was left with his sisters. How many did he have left?

 →

48

© Essential Resources Educational Publishers Ltd 2009

Solve these problems.

1. Michael had a box of 20 jelly beans. He shared four fifths of the box with his friend. He then shared three quarters of what was left with his brothers. How many did he share with his brothers?

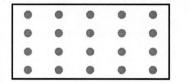 → _____

2. Toni had a bag of 20 biscuits. She shared a quarter of the bag with her friend. She then shared two fifths of what was left with her sisters. How many did she have left?

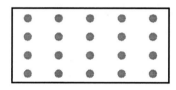 → _____

3. Taylor had a bag of 36 Crunchies. She shared half of the bag with Megan. She then shared five sixths of what was left with Abby. How many did she have left?

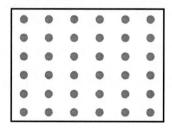 → _____

4. Sarah had a box of 36 bulbs. She shared four ninths of the box with her friend. She then shared three fifths of what was left with her sisters. How many did she share with her sisters?

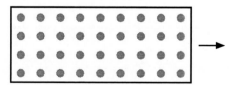 → _____

5. Rob had a box of 16 golf balls. He shared three eighths of the box with his friend. He then shared three fifths of what was left with his brothers. How many did he have left?

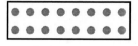 → _____

Activity cards

Double it and halve it (page 51)

The aim of this activity is to reinforce the strategy of doubling and halving.

To **make**:

- copy double and half boards onto coloured paper, then laminate and cut them
- copy equation cards onto coloured paper, then laminate and cut them
- store the cards in a ziplock bag.

To **play**:

- each player has a double and half board
- place the equation cards face down in a pile
- the first person turns over one equation card and places it so that the whole group can see it
- each person then decides which number to double and which number to halve and writes them both in the appropriate columns using a whiteboard pen
- each person writes what these numbers would become when they apply this strategy and continue to do so until they find numbers that enable them to solve the equation easily.

eg, 18 × 5

Double	Half
5 10	18 9

Double it and halve it game

25 × 12	50 × 4 620
25 × 36	25 × 2 004
4 822 × 5	50 × 36
8 644 × 5	44 × 25
24 × 5	84 × 25
74 × 50	96 × 25
58 × 50	486 × 5
2 082 × 5	25 × 6 868
50 × 286	684 × 5

Double it and halve it game

8 406 × 5	4 420 × 50
50 × 840	684 × 50
4 486 × 50	25 × 4
25 × 6 868	248 × 25
24 × 25	25 × 68
5 × 6 424	5 × 482
5 × 8 624	96 × 50
5 × 624	624 × 50
50 × 824	448 × 25

Double it and halve it game

Double	Half

Double	Half

Answers to activity sheets

Page 5
1. 240
2. 630
3. 330
4. 400
5. 490
6. 1 080

Page 6
1. 1 260
2. 550
3. 420
4. 560
5. 540
6. 210

Page 7
1. 330
2. 1 080
3. 550
4. 210
5. 400
6. 490

Page 8
1. $600
2. 400
3. 490
4. 810
5. 1 080
6. 210
7. 330
8. $1 260

Page 9
A1. 10 × 39 = 390
2. 23 × 10 = 230
3. 10 × 74 = 740
4. 462 × 10 = 4 620
5. 26 × 10 = 260
6. 47 × 10 = 470
7. 231 × 10 = 2 310
8. 188 × 10 = 1 880
9. 43 × 10 = 430
10. 10 × 34 = 340
11. 275 × 10 = 2 750
12. 10 × 286 = 2 860
B1. 10 × 12 = 120
2. 10 × 38 = 380
3. 41 × 10 = 410
4. 10 × 49 = 490

Page 10
A1. 10 × 214 = 2 140
2. 86 × 10 = 860
3. 10 × 368 = 3 680
4. 314 × 10 = 3 140
5. 142 × 10 = 1 420
6. 325 × 10 = 3 250
7. 451 × 10 = 4 510
8. 473 × 10 = 4 730
9. 258 × 10 = 2 580
10. 10 × 184 = 1 840
11. 422 × 10 = 4 220
12. 10 × 386 = 3 860
B1. 369 × 100 = 36 900
2. 100 × 432 = 43 200
3. 41 × 100 = 4 100
4. 100 × 49 = 4 900

Page 11
A1. 50 × 12
100 × 6
600
2. 50 × 312
100 × 156
15 600
3. 2 210 × 50
1 105 × 100
110 500
4. 50 × 3 212
100 × 1 606
160 600
5. 50 × 412
100 × 206
20 600
6. 50 × 492
100 × 246
24 600
B. 17 100

Page 12
A1. 50 × 34
100 × 17
1 700
2. 198 × 50
99 × 100
9 900
3. 224 × 50
112 × 100
11 200
4. 50 × 240
100 × 120
12 000
5. 366 × 50
183 × 100
18 300
6. 50 × 4 312
100 × 2 156
215 600
B. 6 200

Page 13
A1. 4 × 6.30
2 × 12.60
£25.20
2. 8 × 12.10
4 × 24.20
2 × 48.40
£96.80
3. 6 × 8.50
3 × 17.00
£51.00
4. 12 × 1.50
6 × 3.00
£18.00
B1. 2 × £9.00
£18.00
2. 3 × £4.20
£12.60
3. 2 × £8.60
£17.20
4. 4 × £13.00
£52.00

Page 14
A1. 700 m²
2. 1 800 m²
3. 440 m²
4. 4 200 m²
5. 600 m²
6. 3 600 m²
7. 2 130 m²
8. 1 150 m²
9. 120 m²

Page 15
A1. 6 × 9 = 54
2. 9 × 9 = 81
3. 40 × 9 = 360
4. 8 × 9 = 72
5. 11 × 9 = 99
6. 45 × 9 = 405
7. 7 × 9 = 63
8. 42 × 9 = 378
9. 7 × 99 = 693
B1. 4 × 288
1 152
2. 4 × 216 = 864
3. 8 × 252 = 2 016
4. 10 × 270 = 2 700
5. 6 × 234 = 1 404
6. 2 × 198 = 396

Page 16
A1. 27 × 3 = 81
2. 117 × 2 = 234
3. 81 × 2 = 162
4. 99 × 2 = 198
5. 126 × 2 = 252
6. 108 × 2 = 216
7. 72 × 2 = 144
8. 36 × 2 = 72
9. 144 × 2 = 288
B1. 8 × 99 = 792
2. 42 × 99 = 4 158
3. 9 × 99 = 891
4. 4 × 99 = 396
5. 144 × 36 = 5 184
6. 18 × 432 = 7 776

Page 17
A1. (60 × 3) + (9 × 3)
180 + 27 = 207
2. (20 × 9) + (4 × 9)
180 + 36 = 216
3. (80 × 6) + (7 × 6)
480 + 42 = 522
4. (30 × 4) + (4 × 4)
120 + 16 = 136
5. (10 × 8) + (9 × 8)
80 + 72 = 152
B1. (70 × 3) + (5 × 3)
210 + 15 = 225
2. (80 × 5) + (7 × 5)
400 + 35 = 435
3. (40 × 7) + (3 × 7)
280 + 21 = 301
4. (30 × 4) + (8 × 4)
120 + 32 = 152
5. (90 × 6) + (6 × 6)
540 + 36 = 576
C1. (20 × 9) + (4 × 9)
180 + 36 = £216
2. (50 × 8) + (8 × 8)
400 + 64 = £464

Page 18

A1. 4 200 + 70 + 21 = 4 291
2. (300 × 9) + (90 × 9) + (3 × 9)
   2 700 + 810 + 27 = 3 537
3. (400 × 6) + (70 × 6) + (7 × 6)
   2 400 + 420 + 42 = 2 862
4. (800 × 4) + (0 × 4) + (2 × 4)
   3 200 + 0 + 8 = 3 208

B1. 1 708   6. 5 970
2. 4 420   7. 4 312
3. 2 164   8. 4 544
4. 1 251   9. 6 000
5. 1 648   C. 938

Page 19

A1. 20 + 4 = 24
2. (80 ÷ 4) + (16 ÷ 4)
   20 + 4 = 24
3. (60 ÷ 6) + (6 ÷ 6)
   10 + 1 = 11
4. (40 ÷ 4) + (32 ÷ 4)
   10 + 8 = 18
5. (70 ÷ 7) + (14 ÷ 7)
   10 + 2 = 12

B1. (40 ÷ 4) + (28 ÷ 4)
   10 + 7 = 17
2. (70 ÷ 7) + (28 ÷ 7)
   10 + 4 = 14
3. (80 ÷ 8) + (8 ÷ 8)
   10 + 1 = 11
4. (60 ÷ 6) + (18 ÷ 6)
   10 + 3 = 13
5. (60 ÷ 6) + (36 ÷ 6)
   10 + 6 = 16

C1. 32
2. 21

Page 20

A1. 100 + 40 + 1 = 141
2. (400 ÷ 4) + (80 ÷ 4) + (0 ÷ 4)
   100 + 20 + 0 = 120
3. (700 ÷ 7) + (210 ÷ 7) + (14 ÷ 7)
   100 + 30 + 2 = 132
4. (600 ÷ 6) + (240 ÷ 6) + (36 ÷ 6)
   100 + 40 + 6 = 146

B1. 137   6. 159
2. 114   7. 143
3. 135   8. 159
4. 125   9. 116
5. 154   C. 211

Page 21

A2. 686   B2. 6 699
3. 1 996   3. 3 596
4. 621   4. 8 082
5. 7 176   5. 3 992
6. 395   6. 4 735
7. 784   7. 6 384
8. 3 591   8. 5 382
9. 356   9. 3 196
10. 693   10. 4 893
B1. 5 584   11. 4 188

Page 22

A1. 209   B1. 169
2. 159   2. 179
3. 159   3. 239
4. 181   4. 169
5. 156   5. 199
6. 162   6. 159
7. 171   7. 178
8. 151   8. 219
9. 196   9. 184
10. 159   10. 169

Page 23

1. 1 020   5. 696   9. 2 016
2. 432   6. 888   10. 1 008
3. 720   7. 624   11. 1 776
4. 630   8. 705

Page 24

1. 24   4. 85   7. 36
2. 23   5. 35   8. 46
3. 42   6. 53   9. 67

Page 25

A2. 1 104   8. 1 224   6. 23
3. 15 360   B1. 28   7. 51
4. 1 008   2. 1 242   8. 1 776
5. 2 592   3. 78   9. 23
6. 1 035   4. 1 935   10. 2 144
7. 2 304   5. 1 872

Page 27

2. 3   7. 9   12. 16
3. 7   8. 6   13. 7
4. 7   9. 26   14. 31
5. 8   10. 5   15. 6
6. 34   11. 26   16. 9

Page 28

A1. 85   13. 74   25. 52
2. 41   14. 164   26. 83
3. 35   15. 27   27. 76
4. 86   16. 54   28. 87
5. 63   17. 88   29. 28
6. 89   18. 78   30. 56
7. 69   19. 81   B1. £34
8. 94   20. 61   2. 62
9. 53   21. 48   3. 35
10. 36   22. 42   4. 55
11. 77   23. 39
12. 64   24. 43

Page 29

A1. 4 011   6. 3 192   11. 4 338
2. 4 956   7. 4 466   12. 6 559
3. 7 584   8. 4 476   B1. £3 904
4. 1 401   9. 4 632   2. 8 838
5. 7 245   10. 2 496

Page 30

1. 2 140   5. 1 722
2. 7 176   6. 16
3. 792   7. 6
4. 600

Page 31

1. 36 900   5. 552
2. 356   6. 121
3. 396   7. 6
4. 1 150

Page 32

A2. $\frac{12}{15}$ 8. $\frac{4}{12}$ 2. False

3. $\frac{6}{9}$ 9. $\frac{24}{40}$ 3. False

4. $\frac{10}{16}$ 10. $\frac{15}{25}$ 4. False

5. $\frac{2}{10}$ 11. $\frac{35}{50}$ 5. True

6. $\frac{4}{6}$ 12. $\frac{35}{40}$

7. $\frac{16}{20}$ B1. True

Page 33

A1. $\frac{3}{4}$ $\frac{15}{20}$ 5. $\frac{12}{36}$ $\frac{4}{12}$ 9. $\frac{20}{32}$ $\frac{40}{64}$

2. $\frac{28}{32}$ $\frac{7}{8}$ 6. $\frac{2}{7}$ $\frac{16}{56}$ 10. $\frac{18}{24}$ $\frac{6}{8}$

3. $\frac{16}{24}$ $\frac{20}{30}$ 7. $\frac{6}{10}$ $\frac{45}{75}$

4. $\frac{5}{12}$ $\frac{25}{60}$ 8. $\frac{16}{40}$ $\frac{14}{35}$

Page 34

A1. $\frac{17}{20}$ A6. $\frac{51}{54}$ B5. $\frac{13}{8}$

2. $\frac{17}{24}$ B1. $\frac{15}{12}$ 6. $\frac{31}{20}$

3. $1\frac{8}{12}$ 2. $\frac{58}{40}$ 7. $\frac{39}{36}$

4. $1\frac{7}{15}$ 3. $\frac{17}{12}$ 8. $\frac{5}{4}$

5. $1\frac{10}{24}$ 4. $\frac{16}{12}$

Page 35

A1. $\frac{7}{8}$ A6. $1\frac{1}{8}$ B5. $1\frac{1}{4}$

2. $1\frac{5}{12}$ B1. $\frac{3}{4}$ 6. $1\frac{3}{8}$

3. $1\frac{1}{10}$ 2. $1\frac{9}{30}$ 7. $1\frac{1}{2}$

4. $1\frac{1}{4}$ 3. $1\frac{1}{10}$ 8. $1\frac{7}{20}$

5. $1\frac{5}{12}$ 4. $\frac{27}{24}$

Page 36

A1. b $\frac{3}{10}$ A4. c $\frac{2}{15}$ B2. $\frac{3}{8}$

2. d $\frac{2}{10}$ 5. a $\frac{1}{20}$ 3. $\frac{10}{20}$

3. e $\frac{3}{20}$ B1. $\frac{2}{12}$ 4. $\frac{1}{6}$

Page 37

A1. c $\frac{4}{15}$ A4. b $\frac{7}{24}$ B2. $\frac{5}{24}$

2. a $\frac{5}{18}$ 5. d 0   3. $\frac{3}{40}$

3. e $\frac{1}{12}$ B1. $\frac{3}{18}$ 4. $\frac{3}{20}$

Page 38

A2. $\frac{63}{8} = 7\frac{7}{8}$ 6. $\frac{36}{9} = 4$

3. $\frac{63}{10} = 6\frac{3}{10}$ 7. $\frac{28}{8} = 3\frac{4}{8}$

4. $\frac{18}{5} = 3\frac{3}{5}$ 8. $\frac{18}{6} = 3$

5. $\frac{18}{3} = 6$ 9. $\frac{27}{5} = 5\frac{2}{5}$

Page 38 continued

B1. $\frac{12}{4} = 3$ C4. $4 = \frac{12}{8}$

2. $\frac{63}{8} = 7\frac{7}{8}$ 5. $3 = \frac{9}{8}$

3. $\frac{40}{6} = 6\frac{2}{3}$ 6. $5 = \frac{25}{6}$

4. $\frac{36}{8} = 4\frac{1}{2}$ 7. $7 = \frac{21}{4}$

5. $\frac{18}{3} = 6$ 8. $3 = \frac{15}{8}$

C1. $5 = \frac{15}{4}$ 9. $6 = \frac{12}{3}$

2. $4 = \frac{8}{3}$ 10. $7 = \frac{14}{3}$

3. $9 = \frac{45}{8}$ 11. $7 = \frac{14}{5}$

Page 39

1. True   5. False
2. False   6. False
3. True   7. True
4. True   8. True

Page 41

1. $\frac{10}{4}$ 7. $4\frac{2}{4}$ 13. $2\frac{1}{3}$

2. $5\frac{1}{2}$ 8. $2\frac{2}{5}$ 14. $2\frac{3}{9}$

3. $\frac{18}{5}$ 9. $2\frac{2}{3}$ 15. $\frac{19}{5}$

4. $3\frac{3}{4}$ 10. $2\frac{2}{6}$ 16. $2\frac{4}{9}$

5. $3\frac{3}{5}$ 11. $\frac{20}{8}$

6. $\frac{24}{10}$ 12. $\frac{16}{4}$

Page 42

A1. $4\frac{1}{4}$ 5. $6\frac{3}{4}$ 9. 4

2. $4\frac{1}{3}$ 6. $6\frac{1}{3}$ 10. $3\frac{3}{4}$

3. $5\frac{3}{5}$ 7. $7\frac{1}{3}$

4. $2\frac{1}{5}$ 8. $3\frac{2}{5}$

Page 43

A2. $\frac{3}{16}$ 4. $\frac{2}{12}$

3. $\frac{4}{10}$ 5. $\frac{3}{16}$

Page 44

1. $\frac{2}{6}$ 3. $\frac{9}{20}$ 5. $\frac{7}{16}$

2. $\frac{6}{12}$ 4. $\frac{4}{15}$

Page 45

A1. c   A9. f   B7. $\frac{3}{8}$

2. a   10. i   8. $\frac{21}{32}$

3. e   B1. $\frac{4}{10}$ 9. $\frac{6}{12}$

4. b   2. $\frac{28}{40}$ 10. $\frac{9}{16}$

5. d   3. $\frac{8}{15}$ 11. $\frac{27}{40}$

6. g   4. $\frac{12}{20}$ 12. $\frac{21}{36}$

7. j   5. $\frac{36}{50}$

8. h   6. $\frac{28}{45}$

Page 46

Each answer may lie anywhere between these two fractions.

1. $\frac{8}{20}$ and $\frac{15}{20}$ 5. $\frac{30}{80}$ and $\frac{32}{80}$

2. $\frac{16}{24}$ and $\frac{21}{24}$ 6. $\frac{75}{100}$ and $\frac{68}{100}$

3. $\frac{28}{40}$ and $\frac{30}{40}$ 7. $\frac{50}{75}$ and $\frac{69}{75}$

4. $\frac{52}{100}$ and $\frac{50}{100}$

Page 47

Each answer may lie anywhere between these two decimal fractions.

1. 0.4 and 0.75
2. 0.66 and 0.875
3. 0.7 and 0.75
4. 0.52 and 0.5
5. 0.375 and 0.4
6. 0.75 and 0.68
7. 0.66 and 0.92

Page 48

1. 2   3. 1   5. 7
2. 4   4. 6

Page 49

1. 3   3. 3   5. 4
2. 9   4. 8